To Tom,

Happy Birthday

and Love,

Brenda III

EDWARD GOREY

THE EPIPLECTIC BICYCLE

Dodd, Mead & Company

NEW YORK

Second Printing

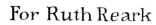

For Ruth Reark

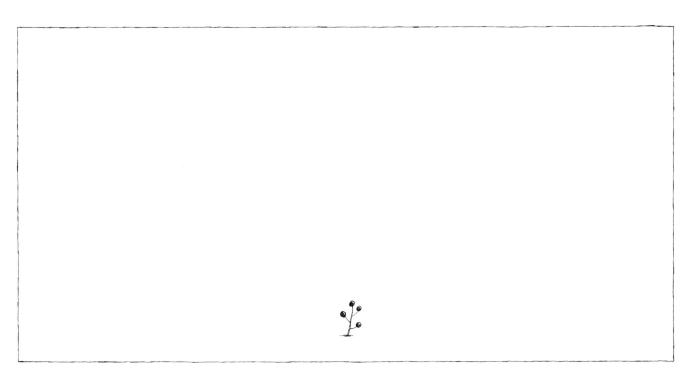

PROLOGUE

It was the day after Tuesday and the day before Wednesday.

CHAPTER ONE

Embley and Yewbert were hitting one another with croquet mallets

when they heard a noise behind the wall

and an untenanted bicycle rolled into view.

CHAPTER TWO

Brother and sister tried to take sole possession of it

until they both fell exhausted;

Yewbert recovered first and leapt onto the seat

so Embley had to sit on the handlebars as they flew out the gate.

CHAPTER FOUR

After that they almost ran into a tree

on which was perched a large bird

who muttered as they went by.

CHAPTER SEVEN

They rode past a great many turnip fields

but as it was the wrong time of year, they didn't see any turnips.

CHAPTER ELEVEN

A horrid storm came up ;

they were nearly *struck* by lightning

several times.

When it was over Embley found she had lost her fourteen pairs of yellow shoes

and Yewbert his spotted-fur waistcoat.

CHAPTER TWELVE

As they were riding through a lengthy puddle

an alligator rose up in front of them;

Embley kicked it on the end of its nose, and it expired.

CHAPTER FIFTEEN

They took a wrong turning and before they knew it, were entering a vast barn;

it was too dark to hear anything;

it fell down as they came out the other end.

CHAPTER NINETEEN

They made for a huge bush

off which they rapidly ate a quantity of berries.

CHAPTER TWENTY-TWO (AND THE LAST)

They returned home

to discover there was nothing to be seen but an obelisk

which said it had been raised to their memory 173 years ago;

the bicycle uttered for the last time and fell to bits.

ALSO BY EDWARD GOREY

The Unstrung Harp
The Listing Attic
The Doubtful Guest
The Object-Lesson
The Bug Book
The Fatal Lozenge
The Hapless Child
The Curious Sofa
The Willowdale Handcar
The Beastly Baby
The Gashlycrumb Tinies ⎫
The Insect God   ⎬ The Vinegar Works
The West Wing   ⎭
The Wuggly Ump
The Nursery Frieze
The Sinking Spell
The Remembered Visit
The Pious Infant
The Evil Garden
The Inanimate Tragedy
The Gilded Bat
The Utter Zoo
The Blue Aspic
The Iron Tonic
The Osbick Bird

THE SECRETS

The Other Statue

WITH PETER F. NEUMEYER

Donald and the ...
Donald Has a Difficulty

DRAWINGS FOR

The Jumblies, EDWARD LEAR
The Dong With a Luminous Nose, EDWARD LEAR
Story for Sara, ALPHONSE ALLAIS
Irene Iddesleigh, MRS. AMANDA M'KITTRICK ROS